Band

by Jesse Levine
illustrated by Kate Flanagan

ISBN 0-15-317243-6 – Junk Band

Ordering Options
ISBN 0-15-318628-3 (Package of 5)
ISBN 0-15-316986-9 (Grade 2 Package)

3 4 5 6 7 8 9 10 179 02 01 00

Here's how my group of friends created
a junk band. Why do I call it a junk band?
We made almost everything from junk!

1

First we made some drums. We used tubs, cans, and a big washtub. Then we grabbed our sticks and imitated rhythms we had heard other bands play. That's how we learned to play rhythm on our drums.

2

Then we got some old pots and pans. We found all sorts of other things that no one wanted, too. We hung our junk from a rope and hit it with spoons. What great sounds we got! Now we could play both rhythms and tunes.

We played our music, but something was missing. We got a box and rubber bands and used them to make a banjo. Then we imitated banjo sounds we had heard.

We made a flute from a bottle. Now we were getting a lot of sounds. Our band sounded good!

Matt and Jean appeared from around the corner. "Your music startled us," Matt said. "May we play, too?"

Matt made a horn from a garden hose. Jean made a kazoo from a cardboard tube. Matt and Jean played a lot of tunes.

All of us wanted our band to sound good. So we chose days and times to get together. We chose songs to play, too.

We played songs we had heard, and we created our own songs, too. Our songs had rhythm. Our songs had good tunes. And our songs were loud!

We were too loud for our neighbor,
Mrs. Dix. When we played, she closed her
doors and windows. But we were lucky.
She never asked us to stop playing. She
must have remembered being a kid herself!

One day Mr. Marks appeared at his door. Mr. Marks is a train conductor at night. He sleeps in the daytime. We thought he would tell us we were too loud for him to sleep. But he startled us. He began to move to our music!

8

"Your band is getting good," Mr.
Marks said. "It's loud, but it's good. I like
lively music."

That made us feel very proud. Mr.
Marks watched us for a little while. Then
he went back inside to sleep.

Mr. Marks, the train conductor, had given us an idea. We would plan a show for our friends and families. We would ask Mrs. Dix and Mr. Marks to come to hear us, too.

10

We played a lot of songs at our show.
When we were through, everyone clapped.
We were startled. Did everyone really
think we were good? We felt very happy
and very proud.

Our group had created a great band out of nothing but junk. After our show, other groups of friends wanted to form junk bands, too. We showed them how. Now they're good, we're proud, and we're all having fun!

12

Band Time

Number a sheet of paper from 1 to 9. Write a word from the story to complete each sentence. Draw boxes around the letters shown. Then make a word from the letters in the boxes. (Turn the page to find the answers.)

1. The friends made a __ __ __ __ band.

2. They used __ __ __ __ and a wash __ __ ☐ .

3. They hit pots and pans with __ __ __ __ __ __ .

4. They made a __ ☐ __ __ __ with a box and rubber bands.

5. They made a horn from a __ __ __ __ .

6. The band played songs that they had __ __ __ __ __ __ ☐ .

7. Their songs had good __ __ __ __ __ __ and good tunes.

8. The train __ __ ☐ __ __ __ __ __ __ liked the band.

9. __ __ __ __

 School-Home Connection Have your child read Junk Band to you. Then make rhythms together by clapping your hands in different beats and patterns.

TAKE-HOME BOOK
Just in Time
Use with "Max Found Two Sticks."

Answers: 1. junk; 2. cans, tub; 3. spoons; 4. banjo; 5. hose;
6. created; 7. rhythm; 8. conductor; 9. band